W9-CCI-892

# Ten in the Meadow

# For Finn Eric
## J. B.

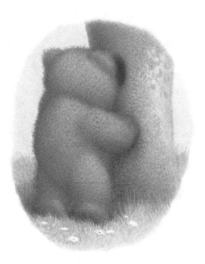

No part of this publication may be reproduced, stored in a retrieval system,
or transmitted in any form or by any means, electronic, mechanical, photocopying,
recording, or otherwise, without written permission of the publisher. For information
regarding permission, write to Peachtree Publishers, Ltd.,
1700 Chattahoochee Avenue, Atlanta, GA 30318-2112.

ISBN-13: 978-0-545-01691-9
ISBN-10: 0-545-01691-6

Text and illustrations copyright © 2006 by John Butler. All rights reserved.
Published by Scholastic Inc., 557 Broadway, New York, NY 10012, by arrangement
with Peachtree Publishers, Ltd. SCHOLASTIC and associated logos are trademarks
and/or registered trademarks of Scholastic Inc.

12 11 10 9 8 7 6 5 4 3               7 8 9 10 11 12/0

Printed in the U.S.A.                40

First Scholastic printing, March 2007

Illustrations created in acrylics and colored pencil.

# Ten in the Meadow

## John Butler

SCHOLASTIC INC.

New York Toronto London Auckland Sydney
Mexico City New Delhi Hong Kong Buenos Aires

Round and round the meadow,
Running here and there.
Ten little friends play hide-and-seek!

"Quickly, hide from Bear!"

Round and
round the daisies,
Bear shouts, "Here I come!"

He's searching . . .

he's looking . . .

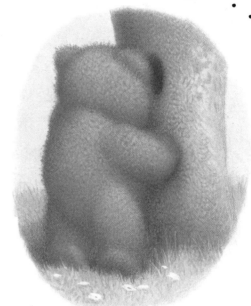

Here, he's found someone!

"Found you, Rabbit!"

Round and round
the foxgloves,

The two friends
take a look.

Among the flowers,
under leaves,

They peek in
every nook.

"Found you, Porcupine!"

"Found you, Mole!"

Round and
round the bluebells,
The friends join in the race.

Looking here . . .

looking there . . .

They've found a hiding place!

"Found you, Badger!"
"Found you, Fox!"

Round and round
the old oak,

Now what can
they see?

Little paws and
bushy tails . . .

Who is up
the tree?

"Found you, Squirrel!"
"Found you, Raccoon!"

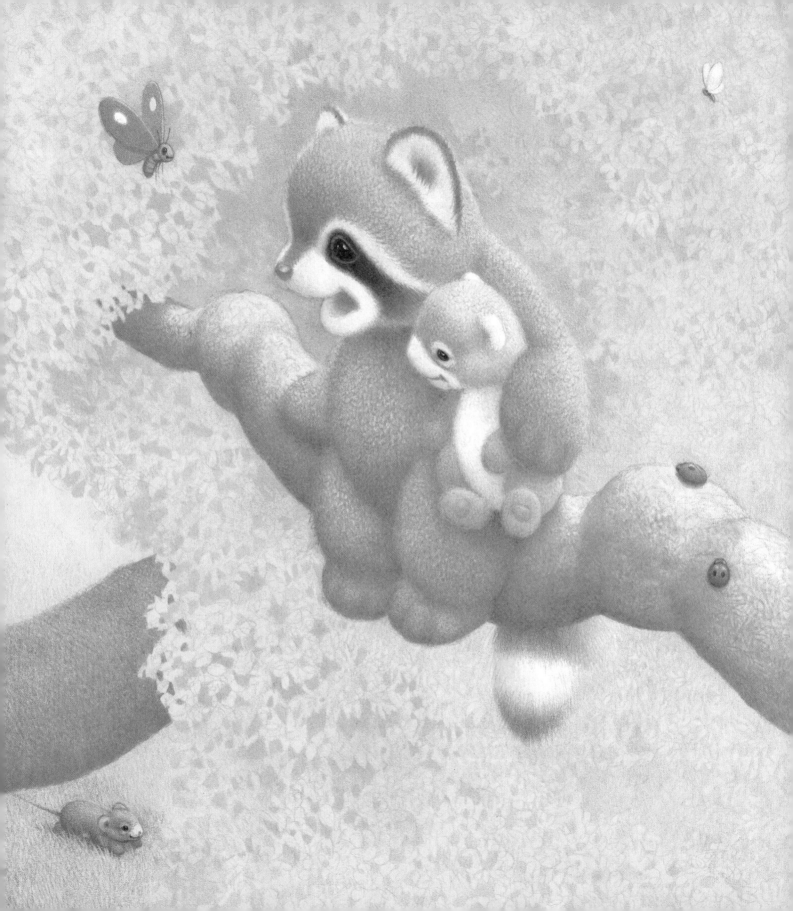

Who's that under the lily pads?
Shall we take a look?

Round and round the rushes,
By the trickling brook.

Round and round the clover,
The sun is sinking low.
Rabbit says, "Now, where is Mouse?
Does anybody know?"

"Where are you, Mouse?"

Round and round
the willow,

Where can
Mousey be?

Bear says,
"I think I know...

Quickly, follow me!"

Back home from the meadow,
The friends all take a peep.
Curled up snugly in the den,
Mouse lies fast asleep!

"Shh, sleepy-time, everyone . . ."

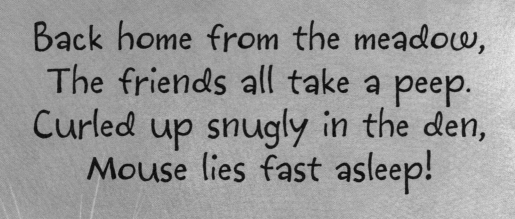

Ten friends asleep together,
Below the crescent moon.
They dream about tomorrow's fun,
And games they'll all play soon.

Good night! Sleep tight!